Sign up
for exclusive
offers at
rebrand.ly/HJP

hobbyjournalpublishing.com

GRANDMOTHER
AND
GRANDCHILD
A Shared Journal

This Belongs To:

_____

Grandmother

My first thought when I was going to be a
grandmother was...

_____

_____

_____

_____

_____

_____

_____

_____

_____

_____

_____

_____

_____

_____

_____

_____

Grandchild

My first memory of you is...

_____

_____

_____

_____

_____

_____

_____

_____

_____

_____

_____

_____

_____

Grandmother

Things I want to talk to you about...

Grandchild

Things I like talking to you about...

_____

_____

_____

_____

_____

_____

_____

_____

_____

_____

_____

_____

Grandmother

First thing I did with you was...

_____

_____

_____

_____

_____

_____

_____

_____

_____

_____

_____

_____

_____

Grandchild

Things I like to do with you...

_____

_____

_____

_____

_____

_____

_____

_____

_____

_____

_____

_____

Grandmother

My favorite things to do are...

_____

_____

_____

_____

_____

_____

_____

_____

_____

_____

_____

_____

_____

_____

Grandchild

My favorite things to do are...

_____

_____

_____

_____

_____

_____

_____

_____

_____

_____

_____

_____

Grandmother

Things I wish I can teach you...

_____

_____

_____

_____

_____

_____

_____

_____

_____

_____

_____

_____

_____

Grandchild

Things I want to learn from you...

_____

_____

_____

_____

_____

_____

_____

_____

_____

_____

_____

_____

_____

Grandmother

Thank you for...

_____

_____

_____

_____

_____

_____

_____

_____

_____

_____

_____

_____

Grandchild

Thank you for...

_____

_____

_____

_____

_____

_____

_____

_____

_____

_____

_____

_____

_____

Grandmother

Places I want to visit with you...

_____

_____

_____

_____

_____

_____

_____

_____

_____

_____

_____

_____

_____

_____

_____

_____

_____

_____

_____

Grandchild

Places I want to visit with you...

_____

_____

_____

_____

_____

_____

_____

_____

_____

_____

_____

_____

_____

Grandmother

Games I want to play with you...

_____

_____

_____

_____

_____

_____

_____

_____

_____

_____

_____

Grandchild

Games I want to play with you...

_____

_____

_____

_____

_____

_____

_____

_____

_____

_____

_____

_____

Grandmother

My wish for you is...

_____

_____

_____

_____

_____

_____

_____

_____

_____

_____

_____

Grandchild

My wish for you is...

_____

_____

_____

_____

_____

_____

_____

_____

_____

_____

_____

_____

_____

Grandmother

Dear Grandchild,

Grandchild

Dear Grandma,

_____

_____

_____

_____

_____

_____

_____

_____

_____

_____

_____

_____

Grandmother

I love you because...

Grandchild

I love you because...

_____

_____

_____

_____

_____

_____

_____

_____

_____

_____

_____

_____

Grandmother

Dear Grandchild,

_____

_____

_____

_____

_____

_____

_____

_____

_____

_____

_____

_____

_____

_____

_____

_____

Grandchild

Dear Grandma,

_____

_____

_____

_____

_____

_____

_____

_____

_____

_____

_____

_____

_____

Grandmother

I love you because...

_____

_____

_____

_____

_____

_____

_____

_____

_____

_____

_____

Grandchild

I love you because...

_____

_____

_____

_____

_____

_____

_____

_____

_____

_____

_____

_____

_____

_____

Grandmother

Dear Grandchild,

_____

_____

_____

_____

_____

_____

_____

_____

_____

_____

_____

Grandchild

Dear Grandma,

_____

_____

_____

_____

_____

_____

_____

_____

_____

_____

_____

_____

_____

Grandmother

I love you because...

Grandchild

I love you because...

_____

_____

_____

_____

_____

_____

_____

_____

_____

_____

_____

_____

Grandmother

Dear Grandchild,

_____

_____

_____

_____

_____

_____

_____

_____

_____

_____

_____

_____

_____

_____

_____

_____

Grandchild

Dear Grandma,

_____

_____

_____

_____

_____

_____

_____

_____

_____

_____

_____

_____

_____

Grandmother

I love you because...

_____

_____

_____

_____

_____

_____

_____

_____

_____

_____

_____

_____

_____

_____

_____

Grandchild

I love you because...

_____

_____

_____

_____

_____

_____

_____

_____

_____

_____

_____

_____

Grandmother

Dear Grandchild,

_____

_____

_____

_____

_____

_____

_____

_____

_____

_____

_____

_____

_____

Grandchild

Dear Grandma,

_____

_____

_____

_____

_____

_____

_____

_____

_____

_____

_____

_____

Grandmother

I love you because...

_____

_____

_____

_____

_____

_____

_____

_____

_____

_____

_____

_____

_____

_____

_____

_____

Grandchild

I love you because...

_____

_____

_____

_____

_____

_____

_____

_____

_____

_____

_____

_____

_____

_____

Grandmother

Dear Grandchild,

_____

_____

_____

_____

_____

_____

_____

_____

_____

_____

Grandchild

Dear Grandma,

_____

_____

_____

_____

_____

_____

_____

_____

_____

_____

_____

_____

_____

Grandmother

I love you because...

_____

_____

_____

_____

_____

_____

_____

_____

_____

_____

_____

_____

_____

_____

Grandchild

I love you because...

_____

_____

_____

_____

_____

_____

_____

_____

_____

_____

_____

_____

Grandmother

Dear Grandchild,

_____

_____

_____

_____

_____

_____

_____

_____

_____

_____

_____

Grandchild

Dear Grandma,

_____

_____

_____

_____

_____

_____

_____

_____

_____

_____

_____

_____

_____

Grandmother

I love you because...

_____

_____

_____

_____

_____

_____

_____

_____

_____

_____

Grandchild

I love you because...

_____

_____

_____

_____

_____

_____

_____

_____

_____

_____

_____

_____

_____

Grandmother

Dear Grandchild,

_____

_____

_____

_____

_____

_____

_____

_____

_____

_____

Grandchild

Dear Grandma,

_____

_____

_____

_____

_____

_____

_____

_____

_____

_____

_____

_____

Grandmother

I love you because...

_____

_____

_____

_____

_____

_____

_____

_____

_____

_____

_____

_____

_____

_____

Grandchild

I love you because...

_____

_____

_____

_____

_____

_____

_____

_____

_____

_____

_____

_____

Grandmother

Dear Grandchild,

_____

_____

_____

_____

_____

_____

_____

_____

_____

_____

_____

_____

_____

_____

_____

_____

Grandchild

Dear Grandma,

_____

_____

_____

_____

_____

_____

_____

_____

_____

_____

_____

_____

Grandmother

I love you because...

_____

_____

_____

_____

_____

_____

_____

_____

_____

_____

_____

_____

_____

_____

_____

_____

_____

Grandchild

I love you because...

_____

_____

_____

_____

_____

_____

_____

_____

_____

_____

_____

_____

_____

Grandmother

Dear Grandchild,

_____

_____

_____

_____

_____

_____

_____

_____

_____

_____

_____

_____

_____

_____

Grandchild

Dear Grandma,

_____

_____

_____

_____

_____

_____

_____

_____

_____

_____

_____

_____

_____

Grandmother

I love you because...

_____

_____

_____

_____

_____

_____

_____

_____

_____

_____

_____

Grandchild

I love you because...

_____

_____

_____

_____

_____

_____

_____

_____

_____

_____

_____

_____

Grandmother

Dear Grandchild,

_____

_____

_____

_____

_____

_____

_____

_____

_____

_____

_____

_____

_____

_____

_____

Grandchild

Dear Grandma,

_____

_____

_____

_____

_____

_____

_____

_____

_____

_____

_____

_____

_____

Grandmother

I love you because...

_____
_____
_____
_____
_____
_____
_____
_____
_____
_____
_____
_____
_____
_____

Grandchild

I love you because...

_____

_____

_____

_____

_____

_____

_____

_____

_____

_____

_____

_____

Grandmother

Dear Grandchild,

_____

_____

_____

_____

_____

_____

_____

_____

_____

_____

_____

_____

_____

_____

Grandchild

Dear Grandma,

_____

_____

_____

_____

_____

_____

_____

_____

_____

_____

_____

_____

_____

_____

Grandmother

I love you because...

_____

_____

_____

_____

_____

_____

_____

_____

_____

_____

_____

_____

_____

Grandchild

I love you because...

_____

_____

_____

_____

_____

_____

_____

_____

_____

_____

_____

_____

_____

Grandmother

Dear Grandchild,

_____

_____

_____

_____

_____

_____

_____

_____

_____

_____

_____

_____

_____

_____

_____

Grandchild

Dear Grandma,

_____

_____

_____

_____

_____

_____

_____

_____

_____

_____

_____

_____

_____

Grandmother

I love you because...

_____

_____

_____

_____

_____

_____

_____

_____

_____

_____

Grandchild

I love you because...

_____

_____

_____

_____

_____

_____

_____

_____

_____

_____

_____

_____

Grandmother

Dear Grandchild,

_____

_____

_____

_____

_____

_____

_____

_____

_____

_____

_____

_____

_____

_____

_____

Grandchild

Dear Grandma,

_____

_____

_____

_____

_____

_____

_____

_____

_____

_____

_____

_____

Grandmother

I love you because...

_____

_____

_____

_____

_____

_____

_____

_____

_____

_____

_____

_____

_____

Grandchild

I love you because...

_____

_____

_____

_____

_____

_____

_____

_____

_____

_____

_____

_____

Grandmother

Dear Grandchild,

_____

_____

_____

_____

_____

_____

_____

_____

_____

_____

_____

_____

_____

_____

Grandchild

Dear Grandma,

_____

_____

_____

_____

_____

_____

_____

_____

_____

_____

_____

_____

Grandmother

I love you because...

_____

_____

_____

_____

_____

_____

_____

_____

_____

_____

Grandchild

I love you because...

_____

_____

_____

_____

_____

_____

_____

_____

_____

_____

_____

_____

_____

Grandmother

Dear Grandchild,

_____

_____

_____

_____

_____

_____

_____

_____

_____

_____

_____

_____

_____

Grandchild

Dear Grandma,

_____

_____

_____

_____

_____

_____

_____

_____

_____

_____

_____

_____

Grandmother

I love you because...

_____

_____

_____

_____

_____

_____

_____

_____

_____

_____

Grandchild

I love you because...

_____

_____

_____

_____

_____

_____

_____

_____

_____

_____

_____

_____

Grandmother

Dear Grandchild,

_____

_____

_____

_____

_____

_____

_____

_____

_____

_____

Grandchild

Dear Grandma,

_____

_____

_____

_____

_____

_____

_____

_____

_____

_____

_____

_____

_____

_____

Grandmother

I love you because...

_____

_____

_____

_____

_____

_____

_____

_____

_____

_____

_____

_____

_____

_____

Grandchild

I love you because...

_____

_____

_____

_____

_____

_____

_____

_____

_____

_____

_____

_____

Grandmother

Dear Grandchild,

_____

_____

_____

_____

_____

_____

_____

_____

_____

_____

_____

_____

_____

_____

_____

Grandchild

Dear Grandma,

_____

_____

_____

_____

_____

_____

_____

_____

_____

_____

_____

_____

_____

Grandmother

I love you because...

_____

_____

_____

_____

_____

_____

_____

_____

_____

_____

_____

_____

_____

Grandchild

I love you because...

_____

_____

_____

_____

_____

_____

_____

_____

_____

_____

_____

_____

Grandmother

Dear Grandchild,

_____

_____

_____

_____

_____

_____

_____

_____

_____

_____

_____

Grandchild

Dear Grandma,

_____

_____

_____

_____

_____

_____

_____

_____

_____

_____

_____

_____

Grandmother

I love you because...

_____

_____

_____

_____

_____

_____

_____

_____

_____

_____

_____

Grandchild

I love you because...

_____

_____

_____

_____

_____

_____

_____

_____

_____

_____

_____

_____

Grandmother

Dear Grandchild,

_____

_____

_____

_____

_____

_____

_____

_____

_____

_____

Grandchild

Dear Grandma,

_____

_____

_____

_____

_____

_____

_____

_____

_____

_____

_____

_____

_____

Grandmother

I love you because...

_____

_____

_____

_____

_____

_____

_____

_____

_____

_____

_____

_____

Grandchild

I love you because...

_____

_____

_____

_____

_____

_____

_____

_____

_____

_____

_____

_____

Sign up
for exclusive
offers at
rebrand.ly/HJP

Made in United States
Orlando, FL
29 June 2023

34628528R00059